Hi,

We hope you like our book.

Tucker   Trouble   Ridge

and Janet

Here Comes Trouble

by Janet Breuer

illustrations by Sarah Hoyle

Tucker Books

Colville, WA • USA

All inquiries or sales requests should be addressed to:

Janet Breuer
Tucker Books
tuckerbooks@yahoo.com
www.tuckerbooks.com
Colville, Washington

Printed and bound in the United States of America

First Edition

10 9 8 7 6 5 4 3 2 1

LCCN 2021901820
ISBN 978-0-578-84889-1

This book was proudly produced by Book Bridge Press.
www.bookbridgepress.com

To the memory of our good friend Bryan and
his wife Faith, who gave us Trouble

—J. B.

Life was peaceful in our home. It was just my brother Ridge and me, Tucker. We lived with our people, a family consisting of a mom, a dad, and a boy named Jon-Chris. Hardly a cross word was ever said in our home except when Ridge would jump the fence and escape the yard.

"Don't do that, Ridge! Come back here," I would tell him.

"You can't tell me what to do. You're not my boss," was always his reply.

He would take off chasing after wild turkeys. They would explode into a firework of feathers and squawking whenever he came close. He never caught them, but he still tried.

I used to chase squirrels, but now that I am older, I don't. My person thinks it is because I'm such a good dog. Really, it is only because it isn't worth the effort. I've learned that I can never catch them. But every once in a while, the urge is just too much and off I go.

We are working "comfort dogs." We went to a lot of classes with our person to learn how to do our volunteer job. We visit hospitals and nursing homes to comfort people. It is a dog's dream job. We get to have all the petting we could ever want.

We are supposed to be nice to everyone we meet. We sit quietly next to them and let them pet us if they want. Jon-Chris likes to come along with us. Sometimes my person tells stories to the patients about the things we do. I love to hear how good and smart I am. Other times she tells us to wag our tails good-bye or wag our tails if we like the person we are visiting, which we do.

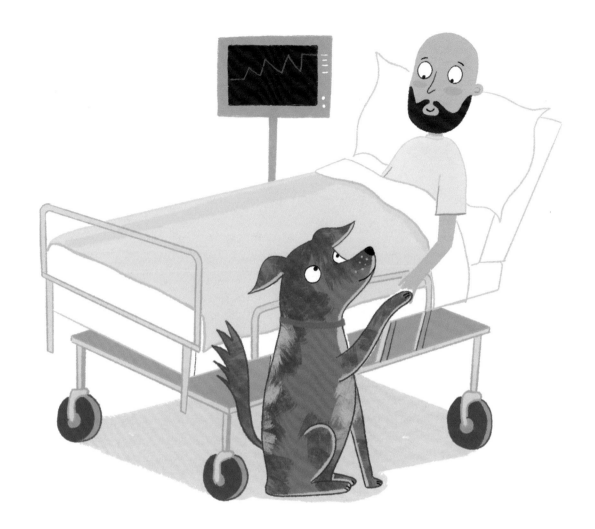

Sometimes when we are visiting with Spanish-speaking patients, my person tells them that we know Spanish. Then, using hand signals, our person has us sit *(sientate)*, shake *(su mano por favor)*, or lie down *(abajo)* while she says the Spanish words. We don't actually know Spanish, only the hand signals.

Even though we love our job, when we come home, we are really tired. It is nice to relax in our peaceful home in front of the fireplace.

One day I heard my people talking about a friend who was sick and couldn't keep his cat. No one in his family wanted the cat. (This should have been a big clue to my people not to take the cat!)

Jon-Chris was so excited to have an indoor cat.

Ridge and I had our own opinions about having a cat.

Ridge asked, "Why do we need a cat? I think things are fine the way they are." And they were.

"I think it will be fun, Ridge. Cats are entertaining," I said.

"I'm not so sure. I don't think this is a good idea," he said.

I really do enjoy cats. They say so much when they flick their tails or twitch their ears. I love watching them stalk real or imagined prey. It is so relaxing to hear them purring. I know then that all is well in their world and mine.

The day came to pick up the animal. We like to ride in the car, so my person brought us with her to run some errands. The car quickly filled up with bags of groceries, along with our dog food. There was barely enough room in the car for Ridge and me. Then my person's cell phone rang, and off we went to pick up the cat.

I couldn't believe how much luggage that animal brought into our car and home. Not only was the cat in a cage, but there was a litter box, kitty litter, a bed, a scratching post, toys, treats, and cat food. When we were just about to start for home with the cat, we found out that she really didn't like dogs.

The cat yowled and yowled the whole drive home.

Ridge asked me, "Is she ever going to be quiet?" I wondered that myself.

"Would you please be quiet?" I politely asked her, but she just ignored me and continued to yowl all the more.

When we got home, my person let the cat out of her cage.

And the trouble began.

She warily moved out of her cage, only to glare and hiss at us.

Both Ridge and I were very well-mannered toward her. We were calm. We politely turned our heads away from her. We tried to make ourselves look as small as possible, which is hard to do when you are seventy-pound dogs. We wagged our tails. We tried to be friends. We didn't act unkindly toward her at all, but it had no effect on her attitude.

"Would you like to be friends?" I asked. But she just glared at me.

"I think we are in trouble," Ridge whispered to me. I agreed.

"I think it will be fun, Ridge. Cats are entertaining," I said.

"I'm not so sure. I don't think this is a good idea," he said.

I really do enjoy cats. They say so much when they flick their tails or twitch their ears. I love watching them stalk real or imagined prey. It is so relaxing to hear them purring. I know then that all is well in their world and mine.

The day came to pick up the animal. We like to ride in the car, so my person brought us with her to run some errands. The car quickly filled up with bags of groceries, along with our dog food. There was barely enough room in the car for Ridge and me. Then my person's cell phone rang, and off we went to pick up the cat.

I couldn't believe how much luggage that animal brought into our car and home. Not only was the cat in a cage, but there was a litter box, kitty litter, a bed, a scratching post, toys, treats, and cat food. When we were just about to start for home with the cat, we found out that she really didn't like dogs.

The cat yowled and yowled the whole drive home.

Ridge asked me, "Is she ever going to be quiet?" I wondered that myself.

"Would you please be quiet?" I politely asked her, but she just ignored me and continued to yowl all the more.

When we got home, my person let the cat out of her cage.

And the trouble began.

She warily moved out of her cage, only to glare and hiss at us.

Both Ridge and I were very well-mannered toward her. We were calm. We politely turned our heads away from her. We tried to make ourselves look as small as possible, which is hard to do when you are seventy-pound dogs. We wagged our tails. We tried to be friends. We didn't act unkindly toward her at all, but it had no effect on her attitude.

"Would you like to be friends?" I asked. But she just glared at me.

"I think we are in trouble," Ridge whispered to me. I agreed.

The cat hissed at us. She would dash at us with her claws out. She would come after us even when we were just standing around giving her plenty of space. I was surprised that my family let her get away with it.

Both my feelings and my nose were hurt one day when she ran toward me, hissing. Then she attacked my nose with her claws. It hurt.

"Why did you do that? What did I do to you?" I asked. But she just hissed all the more. I've never met a cat I didn't like, but this cat was testing my patience.

She would sit by the water bowl and not let us get a drink when we were really thirsty.

She would block the entry to our kennel beds so we couldn't get in or out when we were told to by our people.

She shredded the toilet paper one day when she was bored.

She would purr and act like she wanted to be friends, only to turn and hiss at us. Gone were our peaceful days by the fire.

She even went after my family a few times. They said it was just because she was settling in. I didn't believe it.

I was amazed at how rapidly the cat became the ruler of the house. Both Ridge and I were terrified of her. We tried to avoid her whenever possible when she was exploring her supposed kingdom. We would huddle behind our people for protection, our eyes wide with terror.

We submitted to her every whim, but it was never enough.

At night she would sleep on the dryer above our beds in the laundry room. She would scowl at us if we moved. Our sleep became restless because we never knew what she might do to us in the dark. During the day, wherever she lay, she would glare at us if we walked by. Sometimes she would even sleep on our people's chairs or beds. Then she would smirk at us.

"It's not fair. Why does she get to sleep on the beds and chairs and we can't?" Ridge asked one day.

"I guess our people think that it's okay for a cat to be on the furniture," I replied. But I agreed that it wasn't fair.

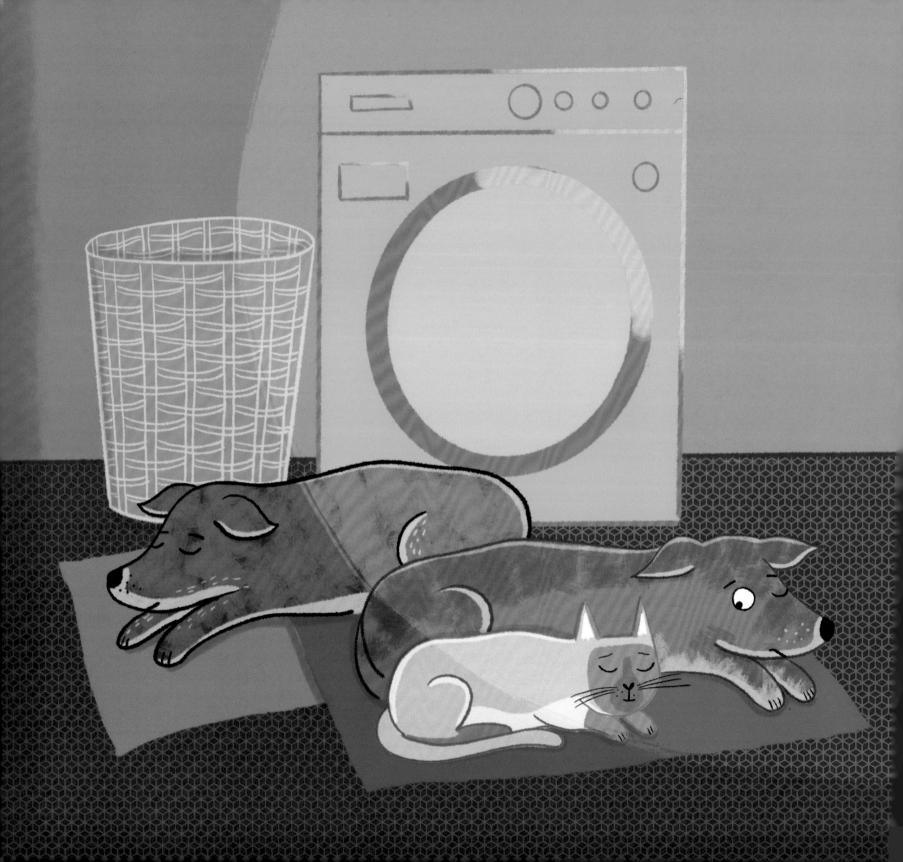

Weeks and weeks have gone by. Ridge and I have been endlessly patient with her. Things have gotten better. She is no longer mean to us and even acts like she likes us at times. Most days peace has returned to the house.

Every once in a while, though, just when we think things are back to normal, she will run up to us when we walk by and swat at our tails just to let us know who really rules the house.

And, by the way, did I mention that her name is Trouble?

Bringing a New Cat into a Home with Dogs

If you have a dog or dogs in your home and are thinking about adopting a cat, it's important to be prepared for introductions.

In general, the younger the cat, the better the outcome will be. Some cats and dogs hit it off right away, while others never get along. The dogs need to be well-trained and on a leash for the first few encounters.

- Make sure that the cat has a dog-free area in the house, somewhere the cat can feel safe while adjusting to the new environment.

- Keep the dog and cat separate at first.

- Feed the animals on opposite sides of a gate or door until they get used to each other.

- Let the animals smell each other's bedding to help them get used to each other.

- The dogs should know basic commands and be on a leash for the first meet and greet.

- The meet and greet should be repeated daily until they get used to each other.

- Proceed with caution by keeping the animals under supervision until they adapt to each other.

For more great tips and additional information about cat adoption, visit **PAWS Chicago** at www.pawschicago.org and the **Animal Humane Society** at www.animalhumanesociety.org.

Therapy or Comfort Dogs

For more information on how your pet can become a registered therapy dog, visit the following resources.

AKC (American Kennel Club) for the Canine Good Citizenship certificate, which is the beginning of training and certifications for a therapy dog. www.akc.org.

Pet Partners is the largest organization in the world for registering your animal to visit nursing homes, hospitals, and schools. Pet Partners has at least 13,000 members around the world, mostly dogs. www.PetPartners.org.

HOPE AACR (Animal-Assisted Crisis Response) is a group that certifies dogs to visit various disasters to comfort both first responders and those affected by a crisis. They have about 300 members in the US and Canada. www.HOPEAACR.org.

JANET BREUER lives in the mountains of northeastern Washington State with her husband, their dogs Tucker and Ridge, and of course Trouble the cat. They have two sons and seven grandchildren.

Janet is a member of Pet Partners, which registers her dogs to visit nursing homes and hospitals. She also belongs to HOPE Animal-Assisted Crisis Response. This enables Janet and her dogs to comfort people who are hurting after a crisis.

When she isn't busy with her dogs, Janet spends time serving in her church, reading, gardening, and paddling large rivers solo. This is her first book.

SARAH HOYLE lives and works in Oxford, UK, a city full of storytelling and imagination. She has always loved drawing and dreaming up characters because she finds people constantly fascinating and entertaining. When she's not in the studio, you can usually find her planning bike rides and road trips, alongside many cups of coffee.